THE PRIZE

A Collection of Stories

by Flavia Weedn

Roserich Designs, Ltd.

Carpinteria, California

In memory of my mother
who taught me
to love

and

my uncle Jack
who taught me
to see

Contents

A LIFETIME

I remember reading in school
    about some great
    historical figure
    who spent a lifetime
    seeking his fortune.

And about a famous
    somebody else
    who spent a lifetime
    doing good deeds.

So when I was ten
    I thought a lifetime
    meant the length of time
    spent on the years
    from birth 'til death.

    That its value was measured
    by the important things
    that happened
    during those years.

    And the only valuable lifetimes
    were those found
    in library books.

When I was twenty
    I was impatient with life
    and with time
    so most of my days
    slipped by
    unnoticed.

    I reached out
    for tomorrows
    trying for a glimpse
    or a touch
    of what my lifetime
    might bring.

I found by my thirtieth year
        that life had brought me pain
        but mingled with it
        was all the joy I'd found.

        Life had been kind
        to me
        for it had not
        left me
        untouched.

A part of me
    thought my lifetime
    was spent.
    The rest of me
    kept pushing
    for what most surely
    would happen
    tomorrow.

But that was then.

Today I looked at tidepools
    and seabirds
    and found an ageless rock
    washed smooth and grey
    by the sea.

    I sat on the sand
    with my friend
    and shared thoughts
    and tuna sandwiches
    and the sun.

    I gave corn chips
    to a seagull
    and watched him smile.

My friend and I walked
    and talked
    and looked
    at people
    and into
    store windows.

We saw beautiful birds
in handmade cages
and I remembered
the seagull.

My friend told me
of faraway places
and we laughed
and bought
Christmas tree ornaments.

I listened closely
to the words of a song
that he sang
about a poem
written on the back
of a leaf
and about a key
to a house
with no door.

At a street corner
    we shared
    the discovery
    of a flower
    growing
    deep inside
    a drain.

Souvenirs, all.

When I was ten
how could I
have known
that a lifetime
has nothing to do
with years...

...only with time.

And that its value
isn't measured by
the important things
that happen...

...unless
  smiling
  with a seagull
  is important.

  A lifetime?
  I spent one
  today
  with my friend.

  ◆ ◆ ◆

Fountain Valley, CA.
July 1975

THE PLAYGROUND

I saw a playground
   today
   deserted and empty
   except for one old man.

   He sat very still
   and to some
   he would have been
   unnoticed.

To the left of the swings
   stood a free-standing
   sculpture
   made for children
   to climb on.

   But it was so perfectly
   perfect
   I suspected it would
   have been happier
   somewhere else.

The sun was so warm
    and so bright
    it played tricks
    through the leaves.

    It made me want to run
    and hang by my knees
    on the bars
    and hide
    in the tunnel
    and pretend.

It was early afternoon
and children
belonged there.

I sat on the grass
and wondered why
the sight
of an empty playground
bothered me so.

The old man
        had not moved
        since I first saw him.
        With bent back
        he just sat on the bench
        and stared into space.

        He looked so very alone
        my heart remembered
        a part of a poem
        about the last leaf
        upon a tree.

He turned his head slightly
    but enough
    and I could see
    he was smiling
    and he wasn't alone
    at all.

    His old friends were there
    young again
    running
    and shouting
    playing
    and pretending.

He was out there
    playing among them
    young like they
    and filling each moment
    with something new.

    All of them
    were laughing
    and playing at life
    like a game.

Spellbound
    I watched
    as the playground
    became older
    and different.
    The magic
    I was seeing
    was all for free.

I heard the squeaking
    of swings
    and the scuffling
    of feet.
    The children were all
    around me
    so close
    we could touch.

The sounds in the playground
    grew louder
    and my eyes flashed
    from the old man
    to the children
    then back again
    to the sun
    in the trees.

Suddenly
the old man
stood up
and my symphony
was over
as abruptly
as it had begun.

I watched him
pick up his cane
and slowly
walk away.

It was I
    who was motionless
    now
    and alone
    and the only sound
    in the playground
    was the pounding
    of my heart.

I looked
　　at the fallen leaves
　　that had scattered
　　around me
　　and those
　　still clinging
　　to the trees.

　　I was strong
　　with the feeling
　　that I had stepped
　　into someone else's
　　dream.

As he walked away
the old man
never looked back.
Not once.
But there was
no need.
He knew.

His friends
would be there
waiting
in the playground
whenever
he needed them.

◆   ◆   ◆

Fountain Valley, CA
September 1975

TWIGS

The calendar
    claimed November
    but summer
    had designed the day.
    We drove
    along the coast
    my mother
    and I.
    Both marveling
    at the people
    who could steal time
    from Wednesdays
    to sit on the beach.

Maybe it was the magic
      of the California sun
      or the surfers
      or the hot dog signs
      but an hour later
      as we walked
      along the sidewalks
      even the store windows
      and the city signs
      couldn't make me think
      of anything beyond
      how golden and how warm
      the day.

But once we had
      entered the store
      and closed
      the big wooden door
      behind us…
      …quite abruptly
      all signs of summer
      had disappeared.

      Strangely and suddenly
      we were standing
      in a world
      filled with Christmas.

The air
    was actually
    a winter's chill
    and heavy with the scent
    of pine and of maple
    of cinnamon sticks
    and the earthy potpourri
    smells of Christmas.

Christmas trees
    stood tall and proud.
    Each one
    reaching
    for the high wooden beams
    of the ceiling.
    Each one
    heavily adorned
    with bangles and beads
    wooden figures
    and fabric fancies
    tiny toys
    and silver bells.

    Each one
    selling Christmas.

The glass ornaments
  made twinkling rainbows
  on the walls
  and the shines
  and shadows
  made each tree aware
  as they competed
  in their silent beauty pageant.

The hum of people's conversations
    mixed together
    with the sounds
    of many footsteps.
    Decisions of what to buy
    for whom
    were overshadowed
    by the beauty
    that engulfed the room.

My mother and I
became part
of the crowd.
Very like
everyone else.
A little lost
in the magic
of the room
and in our own
personal reflections
of Christmases past.

When we left the store
        and walked to the car
        we each carried
        one of the store's
        white printed bags.
        Each filled with remnants
        of the Christmas we'd found.

        Inside mine
        carefully wrapped
        in tissue
        was a gift for her.
        And in my mother's
        a gift for me.

On the quiet ride back
we relaxed.
My mother mentioned
how hot
the late afternoon sun.

I noticed
the stragglers
lingering
on the beach.

As the road turned
away from the coast
toward home
the eucalyptus trees
appeared
on our right.

The silouettes
of their blue-grey forms
stood in all their glory
against the burnt-orange
of the sky.

But...up close
　　　their shapes seemed
　　　tired and old
　　　like forgotten people
　　　standing
　　　lonely
　　　in
　　　an
　　　empty
　　　field.

I stopped the car
    when we saw
    the piles of dried
    branches and boughs
    that had fallen
    from the trees.

    They lay grey and still
    as they beckoned through
    the patterned streaks
    of sunshine
    that spread over them
    on the ground.

We began
　　to gather
　　great bunches
　　of twigs…
　　…my mother
　　and I.

Two women
   ankle deep
   in broken leaves
   and branches.

Two women
    stumbling
    and giggling
    in soft grey dirt
    by the side
    of a busy highway...
    ...filling our arms
    and then the trunk
    of the car
    with dusty twigs.

Time eluded us.

We were
children again
as we stepped over
and reached through
and laughed
while bits of
the twigs
we gathered
clung to our clothing.

While
    we loaded the car
    we spoke
    of wrapping
    bunches of twigs
    with giant cloth ribbons
    and giving them
    as Christmas gifts…

    …gifts of
    gathered firewood
    to burn
    on Christmas Eve.

Whatever
Christmastime
magic that each of us
had personally
felt as children
had returned.

I watched my mother's face
    and saw
    how her eyes
    belied her age
    as they
    smiled back
    at me.

    I felt
    a surge of warmth
    within me
    when I realized
    that for these
    few moments
    in time
    we had managed
    to melt years away.

We were
as two young friends
sharing
the spontaneity
of a rare
and beautiful
experience…
…and
without opening
any store tissue
or printed paper bags
we were exchanging
gifts with each other.

We had found
   Christmas…
      …my mother
   and I.

   Not in that shiny store
   but here and now
   in this field.

And these gifts
    to each other
    we would keep
    forever...
    ...for they
    were not found
    in the twigs...

    ...but in
    the gathering.

◆　◆　◆

Fountain Valley, CA
November 1975

THE SOUND OF TUESDAY

A voice on the radio
     said a helicopter crashed
     this afternoon
     in Burbank.

Two fatalities.

It seems much colder today.
  Wished my heater worked.
  My plants seem brighter
  change in the weather
  I guess.
  Winter must be here.

I wonder
if their families
have been notified
by now.

My painting is almost finished.
Shoulders ache.
Getting hungry.
Should start dinner soon.

The people across my courtyard
are laughing
loudly
and listening
to an opera.
Too loud.
Hard to concentrate.

Local police
      report a thirty year old
      Long Beach woman
      accidentally shot in the head
      by her roommate
      at two o'clock today.
      Died en route
      to local hospital.

Thirty years old.

I was pregnant when I was thirty.

Everything from my window
       looks so still.
No wind
no seagulls
just the silent sand.
The only movement
is in the sky.
The sun is setting
and the clouds
are changing colors.

I wonder if she had a child.

There's that sad old dog
    with that frightened face.
    Body moving straight ahead
    eyes darting from side to side.
    Desperately looking
    for someone
    somewhere.
    Unaware
    he's going
    nowhere.

    My neighbor upstairs
    is exercising again.
    Jogging in place
    on his floor
    on my ceiling.

A five car collision
    has just occurred
    southbound
    on the Santa Ana Freeway
    near Atlantic Blvd.
    Rush hour traffic
    is snarled
    backed up as far as Soto Street.
    Wreckage covers three lanes.

    Highway patrol
    and three ambulances
    are rolling.

Motorists
    are advised to use
    alternate routes
    for approximately
    two and a half hours.
        REPEAT
    Motorists
    are advised to use
    alternate routes
    for approximately
    two and a half hours.

Lisa is sad today.
    She cried
    because her goldfish died.
    I'm glad.

    Not because
    her goldfish died
    but because
    she cares
    and she's eighteen years old
    and not ashamed to cry.

Bellflower police
    report a young man
    stabbed to death
    in a local trailer park.
    Clad in T-shirt
    jeans
    and tennis shoes.
    The youth was found
    at 6:35 this AM
    in Space 317
    where he lived
    alone.

    He was twenty-one.

Now the courtyard people
    are playing James Taylor.
Softer.
Easier to paint by.

    Rick is almost twenty-one.

There was
no apparent motive
for the crime.

A spokesman for Disneyland
   expects record breaking
   attendance
   for the approaching
   Christmas season.

Did you know
that three out of five
children
alive today
will go to bed
hungry
tonight.

The outside stillness
    is broken by
    a siren.
    It is loud
    and
    very
    clear.

Delta is ready when you are
wherever you want to go.

The day is ending
I'll finish my painting
tomorrow.
Need to walk
on the sand
and be by the ocean
now.

My friend...
the ocean.
Whose sight
makes me feel new
and alive
and a part of
the awesome mystery
of life.

And whose sound
delights me
and brings me
peace
and promises
and hope…
…always hope
for tomorrow.

And Datsun saves.

♦　♦　♦

Sunset Beach, CA
October 1976

SOMETIMES

Sometimes
    she comes to me
    when my head
    is already so full
    I think
    my mind
    can't handle
    another thought.

Then simply by her presence
    she has a way
    of fading away
    the heavy stuff.

    Maybe that's why
    she chooses those times
    to come to me.
    Or do I
    choose those times
    to let her in.

    Is she my escape?

She took much with her
    when she first went away.
    Sometimes
    I think she took
    more than she left
    behind.

    Her disappearance was slow
    and gradual
    and now
    I suspect
    no one ever sees her
    but me.

I've given away
    some of what she gave me
    to my children.

    They
    who never knew her
    share her sensitivity
    her vulnerability
    and her deep love
    of being.

Her most personal things
    I've kept for myself.
    Some leftover dreams
    and a handful
    of hopes
    that died too young.

Sometimes
    I can see clearly
    the print of her
    high school graduation dress.

Or hear
    the Hoagy Carmichael song
    that was playing
    the first time
    she fell in love.

I can remember
    sometimes
    the dumb things
    she used to do
    and now they make me
    smile.

And the warm times
    when she and I
    are very alone
    together
    and I realize
    how easy it is
    for her to make me
    cry.

Most of my days
    are very crowded now
    and I forever hurry.
    Even my time shared
    with her
    is hurried.

    But it's time
    I need
    for it is necessary
    to look back
    and touch her
    sometimes
    just so she can see
    where I am going.

There are times
 she seems just beyond
 my sight
 and I can only imagine
 the look
 of her face
 of her hands…

 …and the pure
 and beautiful
 UNCOMPLICATEDNESS
 of her life.

I wonder
    if she knows
    how much
    I miss her...

    ....sometimes...

...this girl
that I used to be.

♦ ♦ ♦

Sunset Beach, CA
October 1976

THE GIFT

Someone stole my car
   last night.
   Damn!
   How could they?
   I feel empty.
   No, more than that
   I feel offended
   and violated
   and angry.

Kind:
    VW Karmann Ghia
Year:
    1967
    Old.
Color:
    Faded Gold
    Earl Scheib Gold
Plates:
    WBL 226
    Pronounced wobble.

    Had original black plates
    original tool kit
    even original owner's manual.
    Nifty, I thought,
    but nobody asked.

Identification marks:
    None I could list.
    All the marks I could think of
    were those
    no one would understand.

Case number:
    512-183
    The investigating officer
    left his card.
    It read Sheriff-Coroner.

Coroner.
How appropriate.
This is a euology
for a Karmann Ghia.

If whoever took it
      doesn't rub Armor All
      on the dash board
      the leather will crack.
      Karmann Ghias do that
      you know.
      There's some
      in the glove compartment
      with my cologne.

      How stupid!
      My car's been stolen
      and I'm staring out my window
      hoping the thief
      will take care
      of the dash board.

For almost seven months
        I've lived in a small beach house
        whose main source of light
        comes from shuttered windows
        which overlook
        a narrow strip
        of parking
        which overlooks
        a wider strip of sand
        which the ocean overlooks.

Most of these months
I've spent alone
or so I thought
until I realized
I wasn't.
I had someone.
I had me.

Old habits faded
new ones were born.
Began keeping
my car and house locked.
Even bought one of those
chain things
for my door.

My car was always parked
in the same place
under the street light
first space
from the corner.
The one
that's empty now.
Exactly twelve
steps from car to house.

I know, I counted.
It's one of the
new habits
I had developed.

So there my car has been
        every night
        parked and locked
        just where it belonged.

        Then, last night
        someone came
        and took it.

Its predecessor
> had been a new Porsche 911.
> Expensive and impressive
> fully equipped
> ski rack and all.
> Gorgeously dressed
> in its elegant original
> Porsche Desert Tan Creation.

> No scars, no signs of wear
> only wax
> and gloss.

When I drove the Porsche
I felt wealthy.
Dollar wealthy.
Like the world
was looking
at me.

I justified my soul
with repeated tales
of why
I deserved to own it.

My life had already begun
    to change
    when the Porsche
    was sold.
    And I felt good
    about selling it.
    I would be free
    of the built-in-guilt
    that was slowly surfacing.

    Guilt that came
    from owning something
    I truly felt
    extravagant.

And so...
   three months ago
   I bought
   my ten year old Karmann Ghia.
   Found it
   on a dirty and dusty
   vacant lot.

   I knew it would become
   part of my plan
   to simplify
   my life.
   A part of my change of direction
   and search
   for peace of mind.

If there had ever been a doubt
    in my head
    whether or not
    this car was right
    for me...
    ...it disappeared
    when I realized
    it had no reverse gear.

    Significant
    you see
    because
    now
    I could
    only
    go
    forward.

It had the look
of a classic
waiting
to be rescued.

Not a super star classic
like Kathryn Hepburn
more of an
Irene Dunne.

They don't make them
anymore
you see
so it was like
finding a rare book
one out of print.
I liked the feeling.

What else
    did I leave in the car…
    that research I'd done
    on children's books.
    A sketch pad or two.
    Some drawings.
    Proof sheets of Christmas cards.
    Lisa's shoes
    the straw ones.
    A box of Kleenex
    white.
    My sun glasses
    and a Bic pen
    fine line.

    Oh Lord, something HAS died.
    I've just listed
    the last effects.

I must get things
        into perspective now
        and stop making
        such a big thing
        out of this.
        Cars are stolen all the time.
        It's not like
        losing a loved one.
        It's only a car.
        A material thing.
        Something
        that can be replaced.

        But...it was a loved thing
        and how can I replace
        all that I feel for it.

And tell me…
how can I replace
my gold bracelet
in the side pocket
or the belt
to my burgundy dress
that temporarily
had become the latch
that held up the back seat
or the Indian blanket
in the back window.

The old faded one
I carried Kookie in
the last time I took her
to the vet.
The very last time.

It's not right...it's not!
I want it back!
Why did they choose
my car anyway?
They could see
it had a mushed-in nose
and there was no tape deck
no speakers.
Just an AM radio
and a clock
that didn't run.

It's dark now.
    As I close my shutters
    my parking place
    is still empty
    save for a tossed beer bottle
    which, to the delight
    of my sense of justice,
    shows no reflection
    from the street light.
    All this about a car.
    How ridiculously sentimental
    for allowing myself
    to become so attached
    to a machine.

There must be something good
to come from this.
Somewhere a hidden gift
a lesson learned.

Maybe when my anger subsides
and I have more time
to think about it
I'll know what it is.

And maybe then I'll realize
    that nothing can ever
    be replaced.
    Ever.
    Because people
    and things
    and feelings
    don't replace
    each other.
    They were never meant to.

    Each new thing
    that comes into our lives
    becomes a part of us
    and adds
    to what we already are
    and to what we already feel.

That's the gift
    isn't it.
    Realized now
    at this very moment.
    All the love I felt
    for everything
    in and about that car
    are feelings
    I still have.
    Feelings that are
    a part of me
    a part of what I am.
    My car was never anything
    but a car.

    And a car was all they took.
    They couldn't take away
    my feelings.

Oh Lord,
    by some special miracle
    let me see a car
    parked on that empty
    parking place
    tomorrow morning.
    An ordinary car
    Earl Scheib in color.

    Let it be there
    just long enough
    for me to say thank you...
    ...and to tell it
    that I still have
    all the gifts
    it gave me.

        ◆   ◆   ◆

Sunset Beach, CA
December 1977

THE PRIZE

There's this man
    that I know
    who makes me think
    deep thoughts
    about myself.

It's not that he asks.
He never has.
He doesn't say it
with words.

But there's a look
in his eyes
and a way
that he smiles
that makes me ask myself
questions
inside.

He takes each day
   in a simple way.
   Some say he has nothing
   but then
   they see this look
   about his face
   and know
   there's something
   special
   about this man.

It's as if he's learned secrets
        that very few know
        or holds the key
        to some wisdom
        he's found.

        This same look is shared
        by others
        I've met
        and I know
        each has found it
        alone.

It's not money
    or power
    or position
    he holds…
    …he just celebrates
    being alive.

The merchants
    on the streets
    who sell their souls
    and the frightened ones
    who hide inside
    could change their lives
    if they had what he has
    but they stay
    on their
    merry-go-rides.

Sometimes
    he feels guilty
    I think
    for the way that he lives
    for his contentment just to be
    and to feel.

    Yet he must know
    it's the world
    that he owns
    and all that he has
    is for free.

Like the feel
    of the sand
    on the beach
    when it's warm
    and the nights
    when he touches
    the sky
    and when the songs
    that he finds
    and keeps giving away
    come back
    as a memory.

It's not really a secret
you see
that he's found.
It's something
each of us has.

It gets lost
sometimes
or just covered up
or we think
someone
takes it
away.

So I'll hold on
    to the thoughts
    that he's made me think
    and I'll be unafraid
    to grow.

    For that's step one
    and the first thing
    to learn
    if I want to be
    all I can be.

I'll never know
    all the thoughts
    of this man
    this friend
    who touched my life.

    Because one day
    he'll leave.
    He'll just go away
    and I'll never see him again.

But he touched my mind
    and I now know
    inside
    that I too
    know the truths
    that he's found.

That TO LIVE
is the game
and I've already won...

...because LIFE
LIFE itself...

...is the prize.

◆　◆　◆

Sunset Beach, CA
July 1976

Flavia Weedn's work expresses the basic excitement, simplicity and beauty she sees in the ordinary things of life. Illustrations of soft lines and color complement her editorials, and together communicate a feeling of hope to the human spirit.

Named after a princess in the novel, "The Prisoner of Zenda", Flavia's experiences as a child brought her to a keen awareness of the need for people to express their feelings.

Her professional career forced a choice between fine art and the tailoring of ideas to fit the "greeting card" genre. She has managed to satisfy the demands of both fields, simultaneously winning praise for her paintings and selling millions of her cards by using her works "to let people know it's alright to feel and to show it." As a result, an everwidening audience is discovering Flavia and her ability to put into words what so many feel with their hearts.

Recently, her work has found appropriate homes with other media. Porcelain figurines, ceramic mugs, plates, tiles and bank checks have all found a unique human distinction in Flavia.

Flavia is a person helping others to share her awe of life; such thoughtfulness will never go out of style.

If you wish to know more about Flavia, please write:

The Flavia Collectors' Club
PO Box GG
Carpinteria, California 93013

Roserich Designs, Ltd.
PO Box 1030
Carpinteria, California
93013

Library of Congress Cataloging
in Publication Data

THE PRIZE
A Collection of Stories
Printed in Hong Kong
ISBN 0-913289-00-0

Fifth Printing